Theory of

Music

Exams

GRADE 1

2010

Theory Paper Grade 1   2010   A

Duration 1½ hours

Candidates should answer ALL questions.
Write your answers on this paper – no others will be accepted.
Answers must be written clearly and neatly – otherwise marks may be lost.

TOTAL MARKS
100
92

1 Add the missing bar-lines to these two melodies. The first bar-line is given in each.

10   *10*

2 Write a two-bar rhythm as an answer to the given rhythm.

10   *7*

3 (a) Name the degree of the scale (e.g. 2nd, 3rd, 4th) of each of the notes ma[rked]
shown in the first answer. The key is G major.

2nd   4th   6th   8th   3rd   7th   5th   2nd   1st

(b) Draw a circle around two notes next to each other that are a 3rd apart.

4 (a) Add the correct clef to each of these tonic triads.

10 10

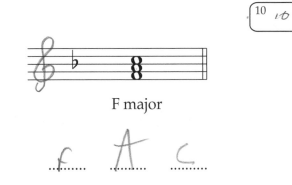

D major   F major

Letter names

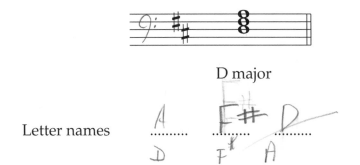

A F# D   f A C

D F# A

(b) Under each triad write the letter name of each of the notes, including the sharp or flat sign where necessary.

5 Add a rest at the places marked ∗ in these two melodies to make each bar complete.

10 6

Kuhlau

Berlioz

6 (a) Draw a circle around the *higher* note of each of these pairs of notes.

(b) Draw a circle around the *lower* note of each of these pairs of notes.

7 Write as semibreves (whole notes) the scales named below, using the correct key signature for each.

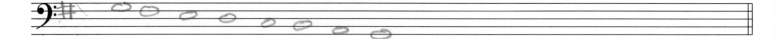

G major, descending

D major, ascending

8 Look at this melody by Attwood and then answer the questions below.

Write your answer to question (c) on the stave below.

(a) Give the meaning of each of these:

Moderato ...... *moderate* ....

p ...... *piano - quiet* ....

the dots above the notes (e.g. bar 1) ...... *(Staccato)* ....

⌢ (e.g. bar 2) ...... *legato* ....

< (e.g. bar 7) ...... *crescendo* ....

10 *10*

(b) (i) This melody is in the key of G major. Draw a circle around a note in the melody which is *not* found in this key.

(ii) Give the time name (e.g. crotchet or quarter note) of the *longest* note in the melody. ...... *dotted minim* *Minim + crotchet* ......

(iii) Complete this sentence:
Bar 2 has the same notes and rhythm as bar ...... *6* ✓ ..

(iv) Give the letter name of the *highest* note in the melody. ...... *D* ✓ ......

(v) Answer TRUE or FALSE to this sentence:
The **4** in **¾** means crotchet (quarter-note) beats. ...... *true* ✓ ......

10 *9*

(c) Copy out the music from the start of bar 5 to the end of the melody, exactly as it is written above. Don't forget the clef, key signature, dynamics and all other details. Write the music on the blank stave above question (a). (Marks will be given for neatness and accuracy.)

10 *10*

Theory Paper Grade 1   2010   B

TOTAL MARKS
100

Duration 1½ hours

Candidates should answer ALL questions.
Write your answers on this paper – no others will be accepted.
Answers must be written clearly and neatly – otherwise marks may be lost.

1 (a) Add the time signature to each of these three melodies.

10

Wagner

Rheinberger

Dvořák

(b) Add the missing bar-lines to this melody. The first bar-line is given.

O. Nicolai

2 Write a two-bar rhythm as an answer to the given rhythm.

10

6

3 (a) Give the letter name of each of the notes marked **∗**. The first answer is given. ⬚10

Bertini

E
....

(b) Give the time name (e.g. crotchet or quarter note) of the *last* note in the melody.

....

4 Give the number (e.g. 2nd, 3rd, 4th) of each of these harmonic intervals, as shown in the first answer. The key is F major. ⬚10

2nd
....

....

....

....

....

....

5 Name the major keys shown by these key signatures. The first answer is given. ⬚10

F major
....

....

....

....

....

....

6 Name the key of each of these scales. Also draw a bracket (⌐‾‾‾¬)
over each pair of notes making a semitone, as shown in the first scale.

Key ....

Key ....

Key ....

7 Next to each note write a rest that has the same time value, as shown in the first answer.

8

8 Look at this melody by A. E. Müller and then answer the questions below.

Write your answer to question (c) on the stave below.

(a) Give the meaning of each of these:

Andante ....

p ....

cresc. (bar 3) ....

mf (bar 5) ....

⎯⎯⎯ (bars 7–8) ....

10

(b) (i) This melody is in the key of C major. Name the degree of the scale (e.g. 4th, 5th, 6th) of the first note of bar 5 (marked *). ....

10

(ii) Draw a circle around two notes next to each other that are a 3rd apart.

(iii) Draw a bracket (⌐⎯⎯⌐) over two notes next to each other that are tied together.

(iv) Give the time name (e.g. crotchet or quarter note) of the *longest* note in the melody. ....

(v) Underline one of the following words that best describes how you think the music should be played:
    legato (smoothly)   or   *staccato* (detached)

(c) Copy out the music from the start of bar 5 to the end of the melody, exactly as it is written above. Don't forget the clef, dynamics and all other details. Write the music on the blank stave above question (a). (Marks will be given for neatness and accuracy.)

10

Theory Paper Grade 1   2010   C

Duration 1½ hours

Candidates should answer ALL questions.
Write your answers on this paper – no others will be accepted.
Answers must be written clearly and neatly – otherwise marks may be lost.

TOTAL MARKS
100

1 Add the missing bar-lines to these two melodies. The first bar-line is given in each.

10

2 Write a two-bar rhythm as an answer to the given rhythm.

10

3 (a) Name the degree of the scale (e.g. 2nd, 3rd, 4th) of each of the notes marked *, as
       shown in the first answer. The key is D major.

10

   (b) Give the time name (e.g. crotchet or quarter note) of the rest in the last bar of the melody.

       ....

4 Rewrite the following melody, grouping (beaming) the notes correctly.

A. E. Müller

5 *Above* each note write another note to form the named *harmonic* interval, as shown in the first answer. The key is D major. [10]

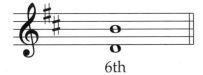

6th

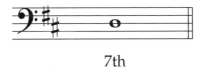

7th

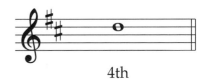

4th

8th/8ve

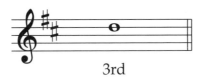

3rd

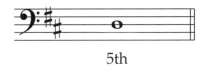

5th

6 Write as semibreves (whole notes) the scales named below. Do *not* use key signatures, but remember to add any necessary sharp or flat signs.

[10]

G major, descending

C major, ascending

7 Add the correct clef to make each of these named notes, as shown in the first answer.

[10]

F   Bb   A

C   C#   G   D

F#   E   B   middle C

8 Look at this folksong melody and then answer the questions below.

Write your answer to question (c) on the stave below.

(a) Give the meaning of each of these:

  Allegro ....

  ♩=120 ....

  the dots above the notes (e.g. bar 1) ....

  > (e.g. bar 4) ....

  cresc. (bar 5) ....

[10]

(b) (i)   How many bars contain *only* quavers (eighth notes)? ....

[10]

   (ii)   In which bar is the performer told to pause or hold on to the note? Bar ....

   (iii) Give the number of the bar that you think will sound the *loudest*. Bar ....

   (iv) Give the letter name of the *highest* note in the melody. ....

   (v)   Answer TRUE or FALSE to this sentence:
         The **2** in ⅔ means the number of beats in a bar. ....

(c) Copy out the music from the start of bar 5 to the end of the melody, exactly as it is
    written above. Don't forget the clef, key signature, dynamics and all other details.
    Write the music on the blank stave above question (a). (Marks will be given for
    neatness and accuracy.)

[10]

Theory Paper Grade 1   2010   S

TOTAL MARKS
100

Duration 1½ hours

Candidates should answer ALL questions.
Write your answers on this paper – no others will be accepted.
Answers must be written clearly and neatly – otherwise marks may be lost.

1 (a) Add the time signature to each of these three melodies.

10

(b) Add a rest at each of the two places marked ✱ to make the bars complete.

2 Write a two-bar rhythm as an answer to the given rhythm.

10

3 (a) Give the letter name of each of the notes marked ✱. The first answer is given.

10

(b) Give the time name (e.g. crotchet or
quarter note) of the rest in the last bar of the melody. ....

4 Give the number (e.g. 2nd, 3rd, 4th) of each of these melodic intervals, as shown in the first answer. The key is F major.

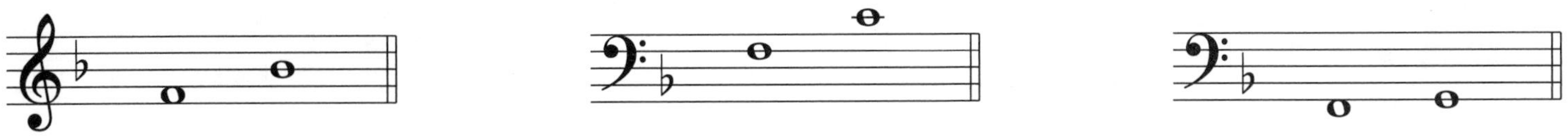

...4th...

....

....

....

....

....

5 Write the tonic triads named below, using the correct key signature for each.

G major

D major

6 Write the dynamics *p* *mp* *f* *mf* *pp* *ff*
in the correct order from the *quietest* to the *loudest*. The first answer is given.

pp

....

7 Next to each rest write a note that has the same time value, as shown in the first answer.

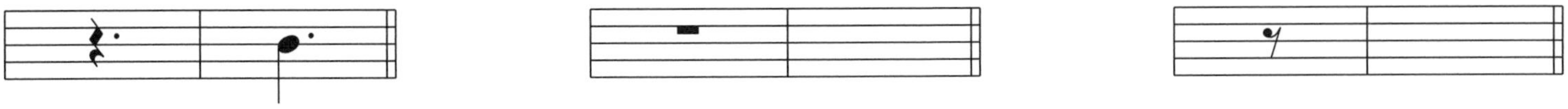

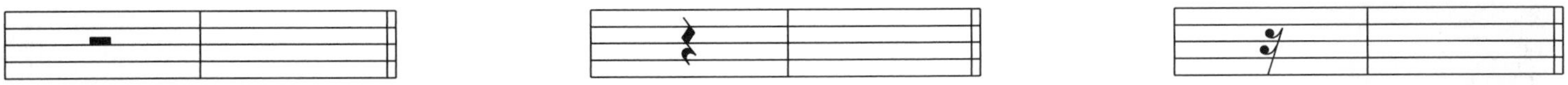

8 Look at this folksong melody and then answer the questions below.

Write your answer to question (c) on the stave below.

(a) Give the meaning of each of these: [10]

Adagio ....

mp ....

cantabile ....

dim. (bar 7) ....

rall. (bar 8) ....

(b) (i) Underline one of the following words that best describes how you think the [10]
music should be played:

    legato (smoothly)   or   *staccato* (detached)

(ii) Draw a circle around two notes next to each other that are an 8th/8ve apart.

(iii) How many dotted crotchets (dotted quarter notes) are there in this melody? ....

(iv) Complete this sentence:
Bar 1 has the same notes and rhythm as bar ....

(v) Give the letter name of the *lowest* note in the melody. ....

(c) Copy out the music from the start of the melody to the end of bar 2, exactly as it is [10]
written above. Don't forget the clef, key signature, time signature, tempo marking,
dynamic and all other details. Write the music on the blank stave above question (a).
(Marks will be given for neatness and accuracy.)

Theory of Music Exams Model Answers
are also available.

Published by ABRSM (Publishing) Ltd,
a wholly owned subsidiary of ABRSM

Printed in England by Page Bros (Norwich) Ltd
05/13

ABRSM
24 Portland Place
London W1B 1LU
United Kingdom

www.abrsm.org

9781848492868
XC
01/15
E   £2.75

FSC
www.fsc.org

MIX
Paper from
responsible sources
FSC™ C109619

ISBN 978-1-84849-286-8

9 781848 492868